STAR WARS

OFFICIAL LEGO® *STAR WARS*™ ANNUAL 2019

Autumn

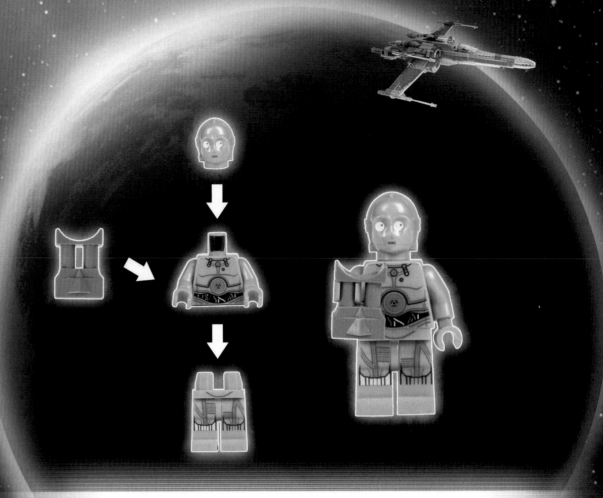

HOW TO BUILD C-3PO

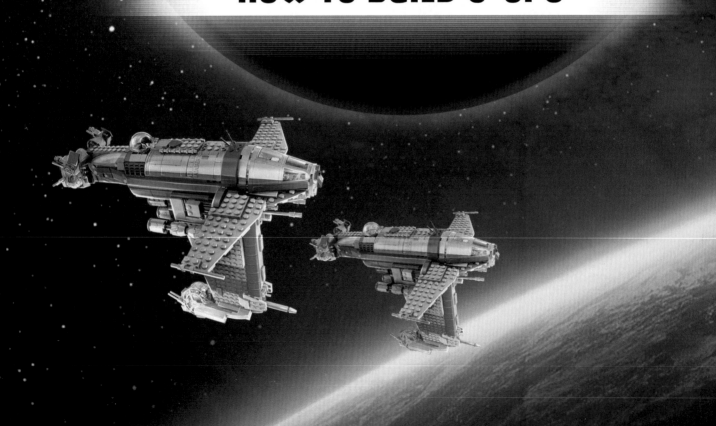

CONTENTS

AS A VERY IMPORTANT PROTOCOL DROID I HAVE WITNESSED MANY BATTLES. LET ME TELL YOU A BIT ABOUT THESE ENCOUNTERS...

THE FORCE AND THE SABER

Once Rey discovered she could use the Force, she was able to stand up to the powerful Kylo Ren. But in order to fight him on equal terms, she needs a lightsaber. Find Rey's weapon in the picture and circle it.

LOOK CAREFULLY. REY'S LIGHTSABER IS RATHER INCONSPICUOUS.

PSST! I'VE LOST MY LIGHTSABER, TOO. BUT MINE IS BLACK. FIND IT FOR ME!

BATTLE FORMATION

In the grid below, General Leia Organa has written the number of boxes that have ships in them at the end of each column and row. Place the ships listed either horizontally or vertically, covering the amount of boxes needed for each ship. There's at least one empty box between each ship. Two ships have been done for you.

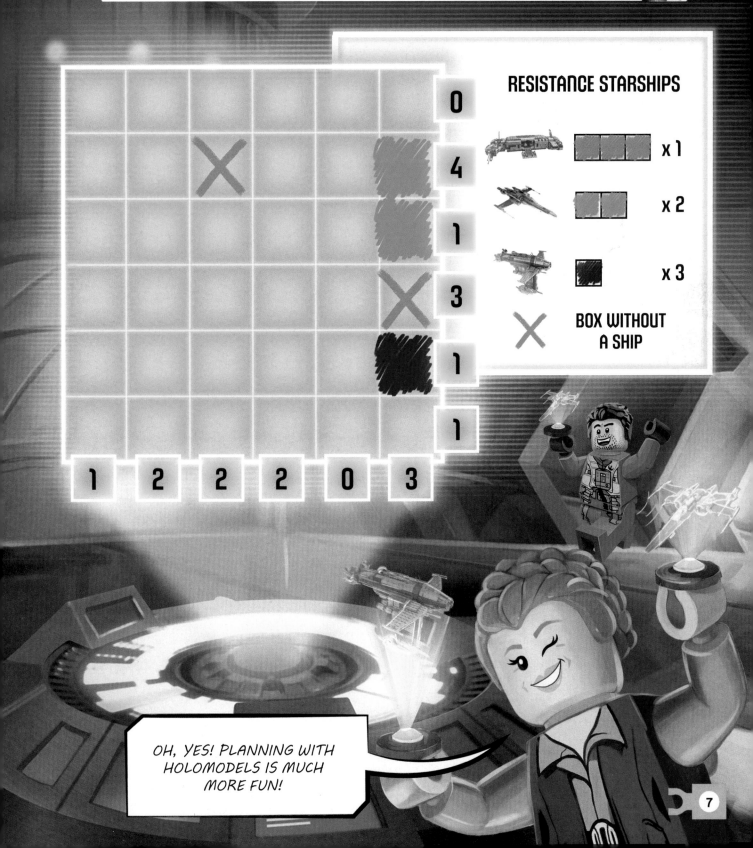

RESISTANCE STARSHIPS

x 1

x 2

x 3

BOX WITHOUT A SHIP

OH, YES! PLANNING WITH HOLOMODELS IS MUCH MORE FUN!

A QUICK GAME OF DOMINOES

Finn is playing dominoes with Chewbacca. Figure out where he can place the remaining pieces so he beats the Wookiee. Which piece doesn't fit the puzzle?

OUT OF THE FOREST

Guide Princess Leia through the thick forest of Endor and help her catch the Imperial scout trooper. Then, count all the Ewoks in the picture and write their number in the box.

START

FINISH

DEACTIVATION SEQUENCE

Han and Finn convinced Captain Phasma to enter the code that deactivates the Starkiller Base energy shield. Did Phasma use the correct code? Find and mark the sequence of symbols from the box on the screen.

ARE YOU SURE YOU UPLOADED THE RIGHT CODE?

STORMTROOPER'S HONOUR. CHECK IT YOURSELVES, IF YOU DON'T BELIEVE ME.

WE'VE WORKED OUT HARDER THINGS. WAIT A MOMENT... ERM...

WALKING THE RANCOR

Jabba's favourite rancor must be fit to fight in case a Jedi Knight turns up. Malakili should take the beast for a walk, but he doesn't know which chain is attached to his pet's collar. Help him find it and circle your answer.

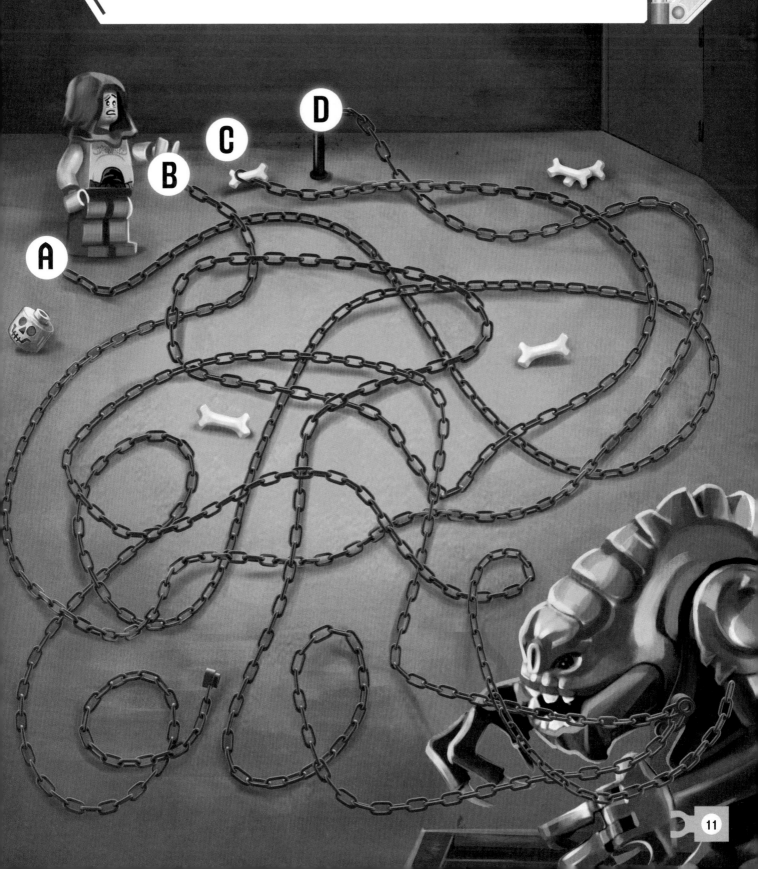

GENERAL ORDER

Master Kenobi has discovered that General Grievous does his combat moves in a specific order. Figure out Grevious's subsequent actions, writing the correct numbers in the empty spaces.

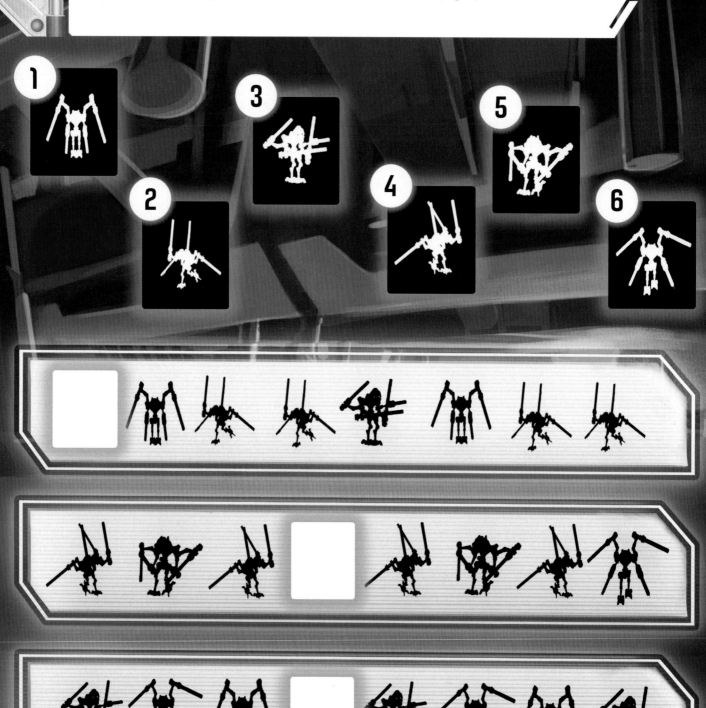

THE BEST DEFENCE

To know your opponent's move is one thing, but to choose the right defensive tactics is another. Study Grievous's attacks and apply suitable blocks to help Obi-Wan defeat the general.

DEFENCE:

ATTACK:

1

↙	BLOCK THE STRIKE FROM BEHIND

Ŧ	STRIKE FROM BEHIND

2

▢	BLOCK THE FORWARD STRIKE

⅂	FORWARD STRIKE

3

⊐	BLOCK THE JUMP STRIKE

Ⅎ	JUMP STRIKE

WHAT IS THIS... AEROBICS OR SOMETHING?

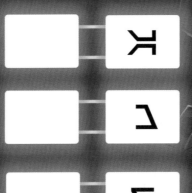

WHERE'S MY WEAPON STORAGE?

Look at the Resistance base plan and find the two places where Finn and Rose can get the types of weapons they need. The codes on the tags will help you find the two rooms.

MASTER VS. APPRENTICE: FIRST CLASH

With age, Anakin Skywalker hasn't lost his love for racing. Untangle his and Obi-Wan Kenobi's trails to see who has won this space competition.

START 1 2

START 3 4

FINISH

CAMOUFLAGE MASTERS

Compare the camouflage skills of stormtroopers vs. the rebels. Eight stormtroopers are hiding below. Start a stopwatch to check how long it takes you to find them all. Write the result in the box.

OH, DEAR, DEAR! LOOKING AT THIS SCENE MAKES MY PHOTORECEPTORS FREEZE. I MUST WARM UP A BIT.

YOUR TIME:

Ready? Now here's a similar task: find eight rebels hiding in this picture. Remember to measure your time and write the result in the second box. Who took longer to find? They're the camouflage masters!

YOUR TIME:

HUTT VS. HUTT

Jabba and Graballa have sent their bounty hunters on a mission. Boba Fett needs to collect all of the gorgs, while Dengar has to do the same with all the boxes with parts. Complete the mazes, writing how long it takes you below each one.

I NEVER LIKED YOU, COUSIN, AND IF DENGAR WINS I DON'T THINK I'LL EVER LIKE YOU.

START

FINISH

YOUR TIME:

18

Why not ask a friend to play the game with you?
Each of you pick a bounty hunter, and the one who makes
it to the finish of their own maze first is the winner.

START

FINISH

YOUR TIME:

19

MASTER VS. APPRENTICE: SECOND CLASH

Who would've thought it would come to this? Anakin gave in to the dark side of the Force and turned against Obi-Wan. Look at the two scenes from their duel and find ten differences between them.

I WONDER WHY ANAKIN HAD RINGS ROUND HIS EYES. IS IT BECAUSE YOU DON'T SEE WELL ON THE DARK SIDE AND YOU MUST SQUINT?

BATTLE OF MINDS

A duel between a Jedi Master and a Sith Lord is not an ordinary fight!
Yoda is trying to read his opponent's mind before battle. Connect the
dots to discover what's on the evil Emperor's mind.

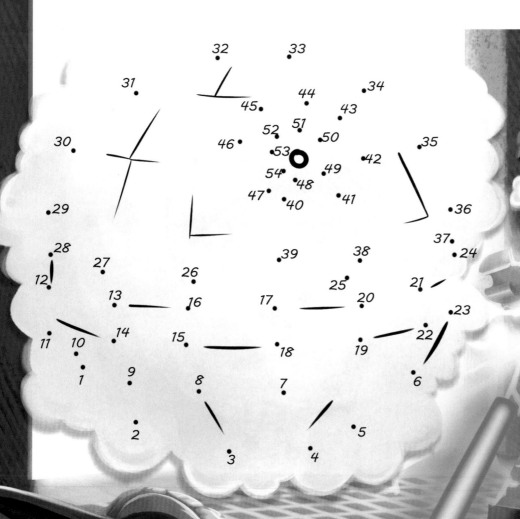

A MEATBALL,
IS IT? CLOUDED, HIS
THOUGHTS ARE...

ANOTHER WIN

Han and Lando enjoy playing card games. Han had a stroke of luck and won another starship from Lando. Use the colour code to fill in the picture and find out what ship it was.

1   2   3   4

HA! IT'LL BE PERFECT FOR MY SON'S FLYING LESSONS! I MEAN, IF I EVER HAVE A SON...

UNLUCKY HIT

Paige's bomber got hit and lost a few parts. Compare her starship to the image on the holoscreen, then find six missing parts drifting among the space junk.

A DROID'S LIFE

... AND THEN MY MAKER PROGRAMMED ME FOR PROTOCOL.

A PERFECT CHOICE! HOW COMFORTABLE! A PROTOCOL DROID'S BASIC FUNCTION IS TO COMMUNICATE WITH PEOPLE...

... OR FELLOW DROIDS...

I AM FLUENT IN OVER SIX MILLION FORMS OF COMMUNICATION...

QUIET! PUT A RESTRAINING BOLT ON THIS ONE!

... OR OTHER FRIENDLY CREATURES.

UTINNI!!!

TARGET LOCATION

Help Poe Dameron locate his targets by finding all three formations of First Order starships on his radar. Then look at the space battle, count the enemy TIE fighters and write the number in the box.

> COME IN, BASE! I'M FLYING BLIND. HELP ME LOCK IN ON THOSE BAD GUYS!

FIRST ORDER FLEET:

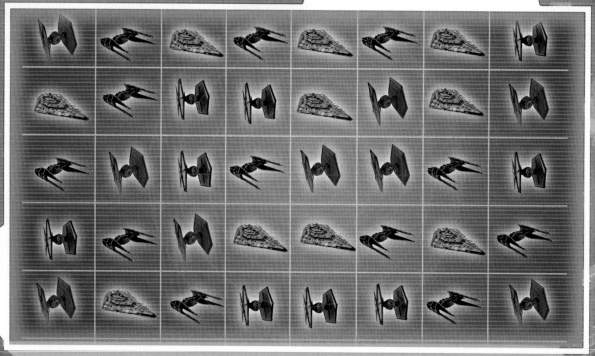

DESIGN YOUR OWN DROIDS

Droids are really useful and everyone in the galaxy should have one. Create your own droid army by copying these four droids into their respective grids. Why not also add some parts of your own to make them truly unique?

BATTLE DROID

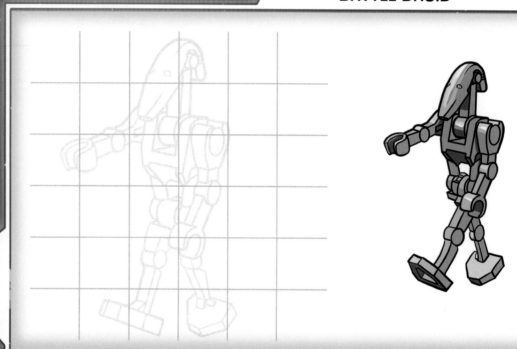

PROBE DROID

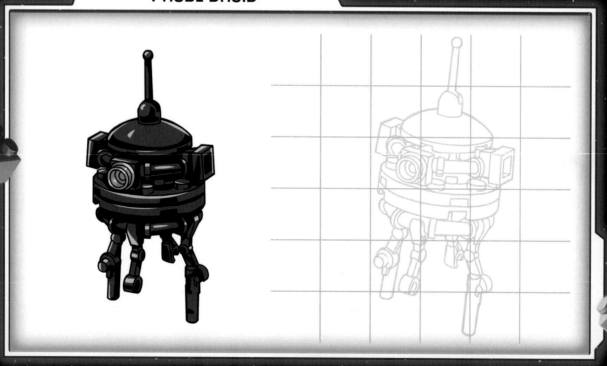

DESTROYER DROID

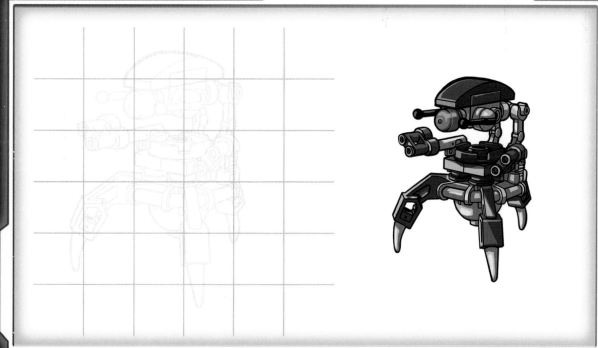

TREADWELL REPAIR DROID

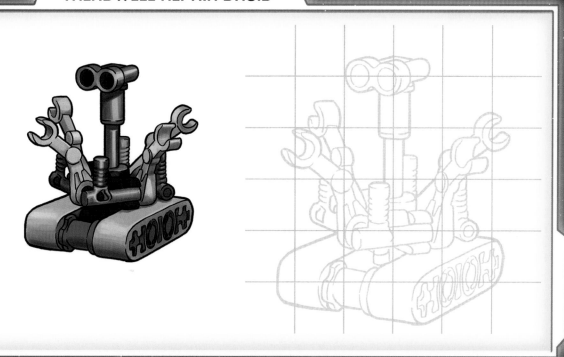

Darth Vader facing his former master? Hard to believe it, but it's true!
I even took photos as proof but something strange happened.
Each image has a small detail making it different from the real scene.
Can you spot them?

CLEVER ESCAPE

Meeting face-to-face with a squadron of TIE fighters and escaping without a scratch is something! Number the below pictures 1 to 4 and retell Han and Chewie's story to Greedo.

ROGUE POSITIONS

Space combat is about to begin! Determine the battle formation by drawing as many X-wing fighters inside the grid as indicated by the numbers next to every row and column.

BLOCKED TRANSMISSION

We need to jam the Imperial spy signal! Follow the blue and purple Force Lightning bolts and write down the numbers you come across – they'll form a code that will confuse the evil Emperor.

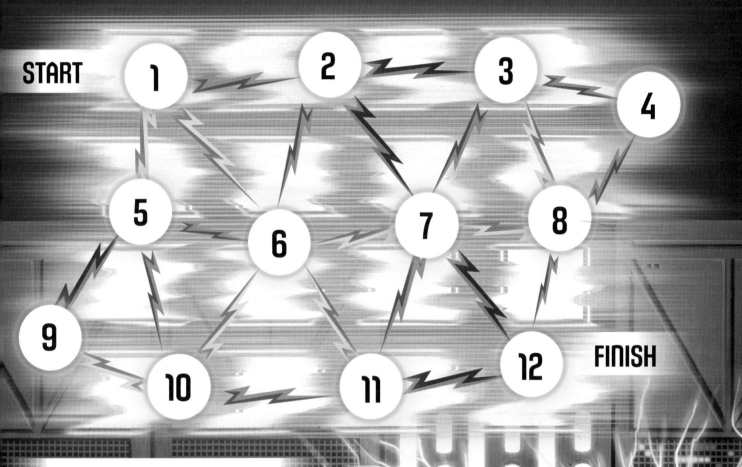

START

1 2 3 4

5 6 7 8

9 10 11 12 FINISH

CONFUSION CODE:

EPIC BATTLE

Galactic skirmishes are often very dramatic. The situation on the battlefield can change in an instant. Look at the two pictures taken a few minutes between each other and find ten elements that changed.

FURRY AND THE FURIOUS

Chewbacca has already learned how annoying porgs can be. One of them just snatched his sandwich! Help the Wookiee find the small thief. The greedy porg looks different to all the others.

THIS ISN'T THE DROID YOU'RE LOOKING FOR

A Teedo wants poor BB-8! Help Rey distract him and draw his attention to the derelict ship parts. This way, the tiny droid will be able to escape. Write down the number of parts inside the frames below.

RATHTAR'S ESCAPE

A dangerous rathtar is on the loose! Bring the monster back to its cage by completing the missing pipe fragments. Draw the given parts inside the right spaces to complete the maze. Be careful – don't let the creature bump into Han or Chewbacca!

THE GENERAL'S SPEECH

General Hux loves rallying his troops. His passionate speeches would never work so well without First Order flags proudly fluttering in the wind. Look at the big First Order symbol on the right and find the identical sign amongst its copies below.

A TOUGH CROWD

It seems not all stormtroopers are paying attention to Hux's speech. Five of them are doing something completely different! Find them among all the listeners before Hux does or he'll surely be angry!

IS IT TRUE HE'S YELLING SO LOUD BECAUSE YOU CAN'T HEAR ANYTHING IN THOSE HELMETS?

DID YOU SAY SOMETHING?

KYLO'S TROUBLE

Kylo Ren can't concentrate on his evil plots. His thoughts dwell too much on a certain person. Count the characters below. The one who appears the most is distracting Kylo Ren.

HAN SOLO

LEIA

DARTH VADER

FINN

REY

SNOKE

A KEEN EYE

Anakin decides to prove himself in the young Padawan training program. Perhaps you'd also like to test your observation skills? All you need to do is find all the brick arrangements as shown in the frame.

WINTER GEAR

With the harsh environment on the ice planet of Hoth, fighting the Empire requires extra preparations. Leia and Luke must collect the right set of gear before going into battle. Find all the items on their list.

HUNTER'S GAME

Han has it hard with all the bounty hunters trying to track him down. But he got lucky this time – Boba Fett is proposing a temporary truce, if Han can help him solve this puzzle. Perhaps you can assist him in this task?

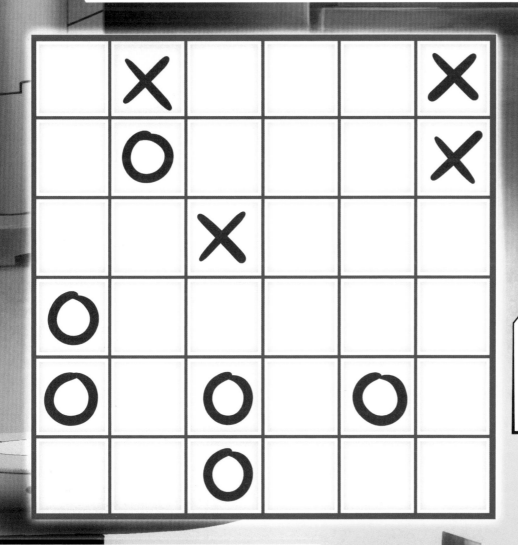

THE MOS EISLEY CANTINA IS A HORRID PLACE. I DON'T RECOMMEND IT AT ALL. THEY DIDN'T EVEN LET ME IN!

RULES:
1. There are no more than two consecutive X's or O's in a row or a column.
2. The X's and O's must appear three times each in every row and column.

TWO PILOTS, ONE SHIP

Lead Rey to the planet Ahch-To. From the START square, draw a line along the track as fast as you can, without touching the sides of the track or taking the pen off the page. Write your time in the box below.

YOUR TIME:

Now work out a secret smuggling route in hyperspace for Han Solo. Jump between neighbouring star systems only through wormholes of the same colour and with the same symbol. Remember: you can visit the star systems just once.

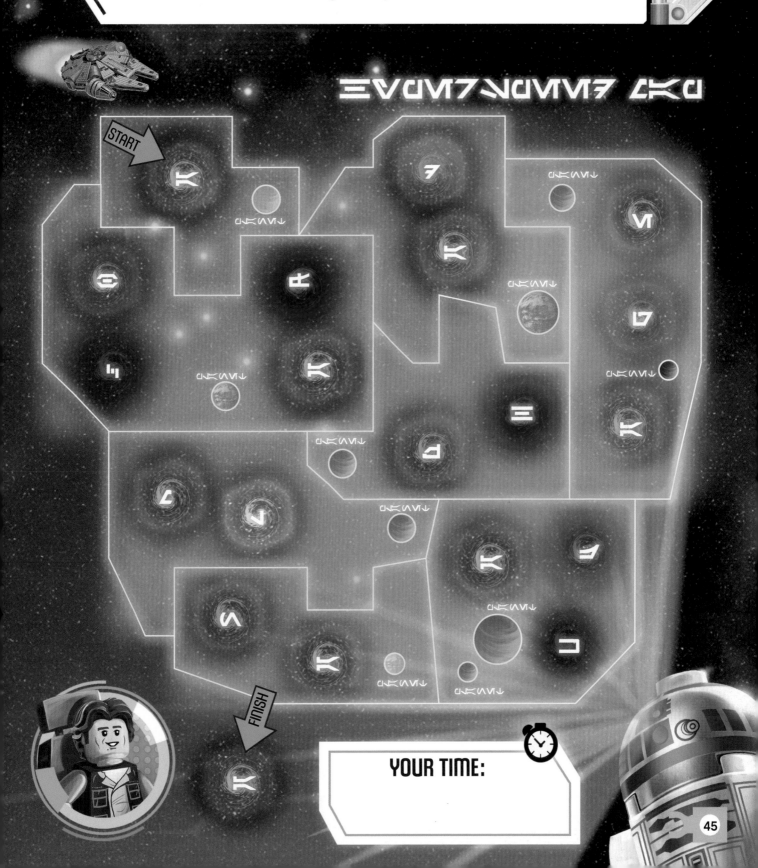

YOUR TIME:

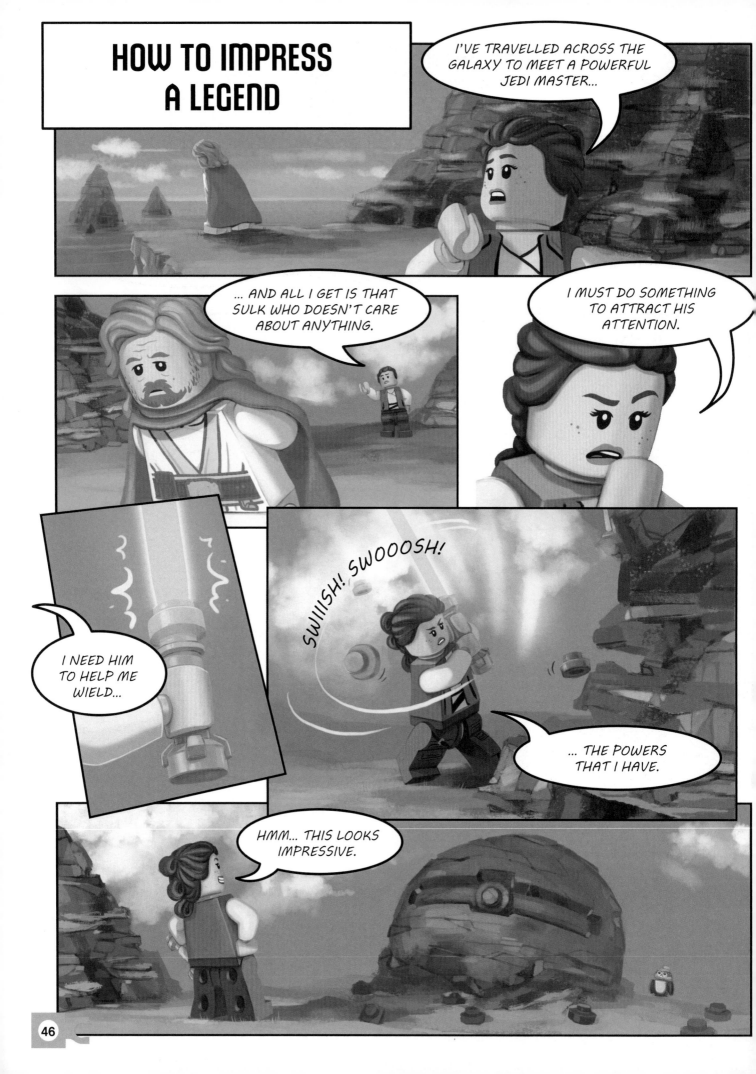

OBVIOUSLY, NOT TO HIM.

MAYBE IF HE SEES SOMETHING MORE FAMILIAR...

LET'S SEE IF THIS WORKS!

HE'S STILL NOT IMPRESSED...

OKAY! ONE MORE TRY!

TA-DAAA!!!

CAN HE EVEN CARE LESS?!

I'M GLAD AT LEAST YOU LIKE IT, GUYS.

AN ENCODED MESSAGE

Incoming encrypted message from the Resistance: Finn and Rose are to join the battle against the First Order as soon as possible. Follow the given instructions to decipher where they will be heading.

START

Now that you know which planet is their destination, find it on the star map and write down its coordinates.

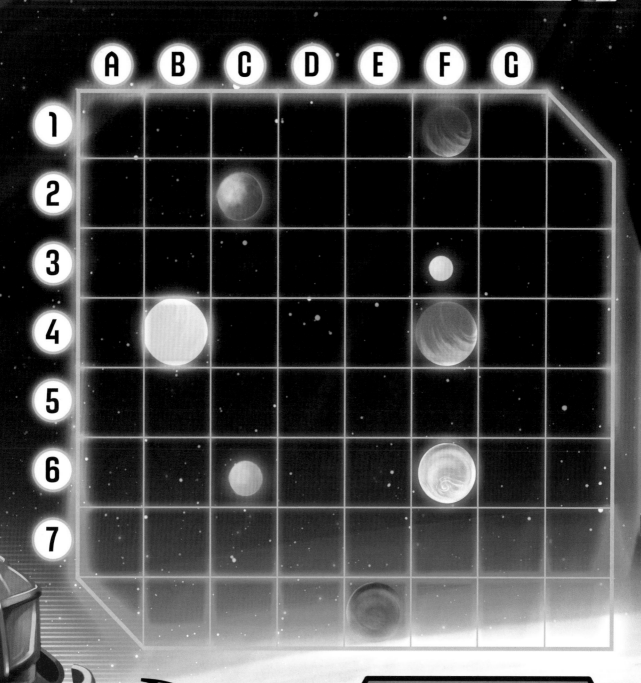

MY PROGRAMMING CAN DECIPHER ANY MESSAGE!

COORDINATES:

JEDI STUDENTS

Solve the riddles and discover, from first to last, the order in which these warriors completed their Jedi training. This way you'll also find out who was each student's master!

1. YODA NEITHER TRAINED LAST NOR THE THIRD.

2. OBI-WAN WAS TRAINED BY A JEDI KNIGHT WIELDING A GREEN LIGHTSABER.

3. THE GREY-HAIRED CHARACTER DIDN'T TRAIN ANAKIN.

4. OBI-WAN WAS THE FOURTH OF THESE CHARACTERS TO COMPLETE HIS TRAINING.

5. ANAKIN DIDN'T TRAIN SECOND.

6. YODA WASN'T QUI-GON JINN'S MASTER.

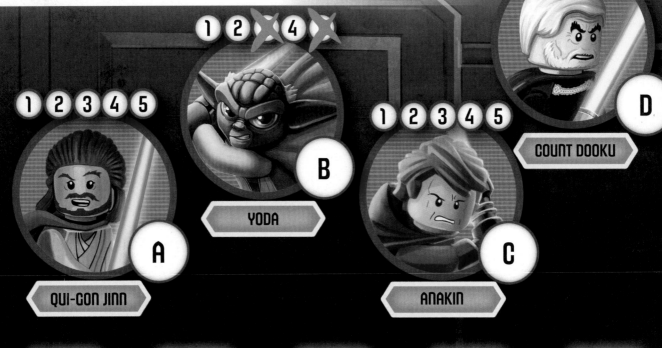

1 2 3 4 5 OBI-WAN KENOBI — E

1 2 3 4 5 COUNT DOOKU — D

1 2 ✗ 4 ✗ YODA — B

1 2 3 4 5 QUI-GON JINN — A

1 2 3 4 5 ANAKIN — C

CHALLENGING THE MASTER

Rey decided to challenge Luke to a Force-powered rock-crushing duel. The rock-breaking techniques used by both heroes are shown in frames below. Count the rocks in the picture to find out who crushed the most.

ODD ONE OUT

Each group of photos show vehicles that are supposed to have something in common. But there is one vehicle in each group that doesn't match the others. Mark the odd one in each group.

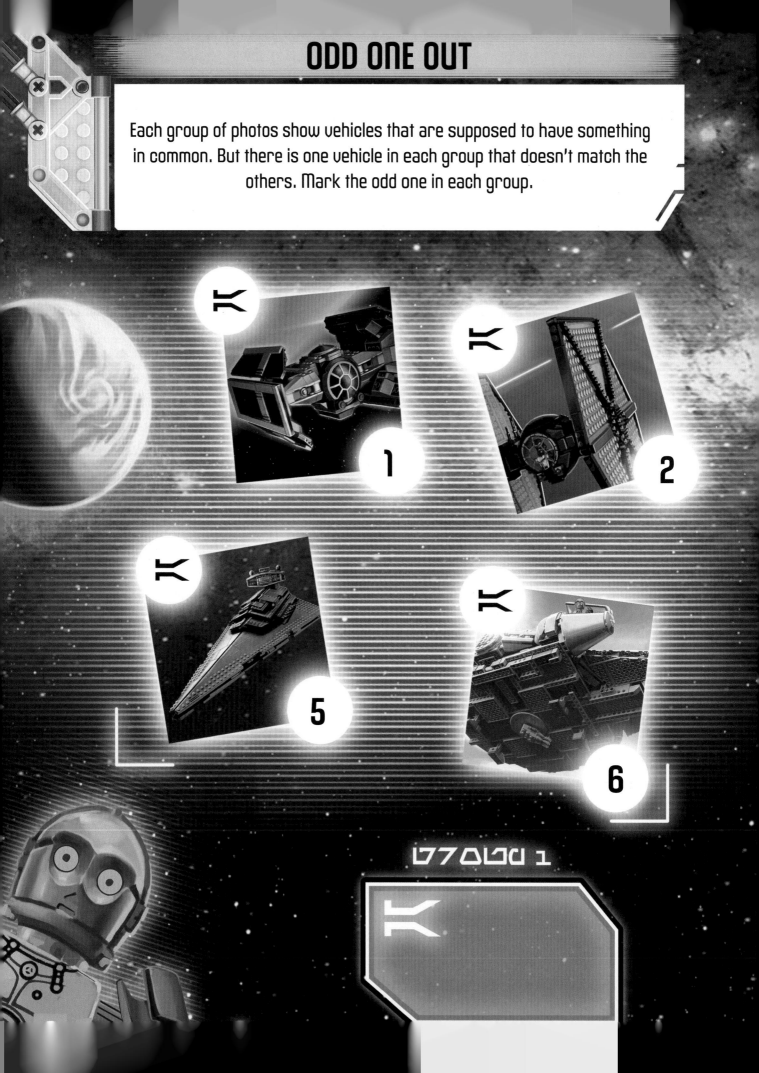

1

2

5

6

ᒍᔑ口ᒍᒍ 1

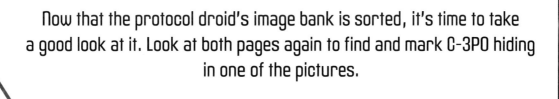

Now that the protocol droid's image bank is sorted, it's time to take a good look at it. Look at both pages again to find and mark C-3PO hiding in one of the pictures.

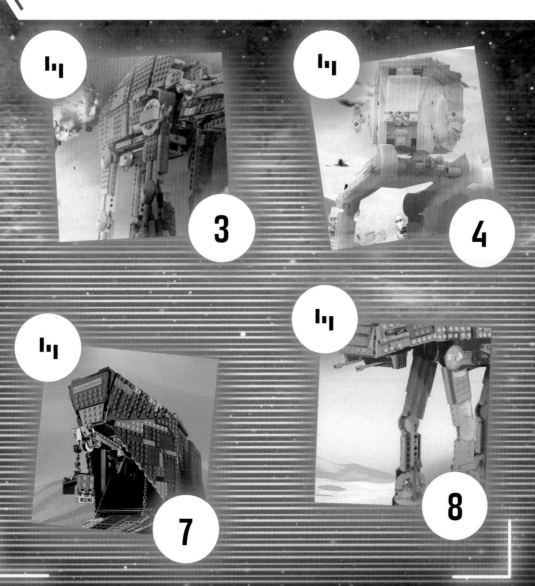

DUEL ON NABOO

During their fight with Darth Maul, young Obi-Wan and Qui-Gon Jinn were separated by a system of force fields. Help the Padawan quickly reach his master by leading him through the barriers emitting yellow light.

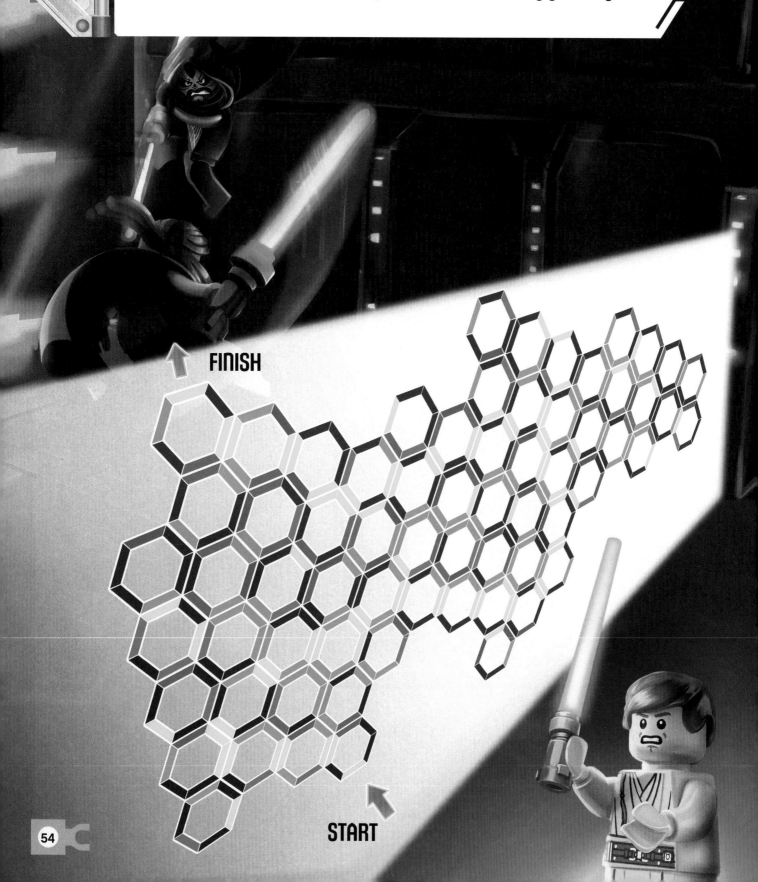

FINISH

START

THE BATTLE ON CRAIT

During the battle against the First Order, Major Ematt manned one of the cannons! Look at the macrobinocular images and find the close-up that matches the bigger image. This will help the Major hit his target.

A

B

C

OPEN FIRE!

The First Order better watch out! Poe is coming for them.
Look at the instructions and circle the four buttons which
activate the blaster cannon.

BATTLE STATIONS!

The Star Destroyer crew is getting ready for battle. See if all the troopers manned their stations. Complete the grid with letters representing the right characters so that there are four different First Order troopers standing in each row and column.

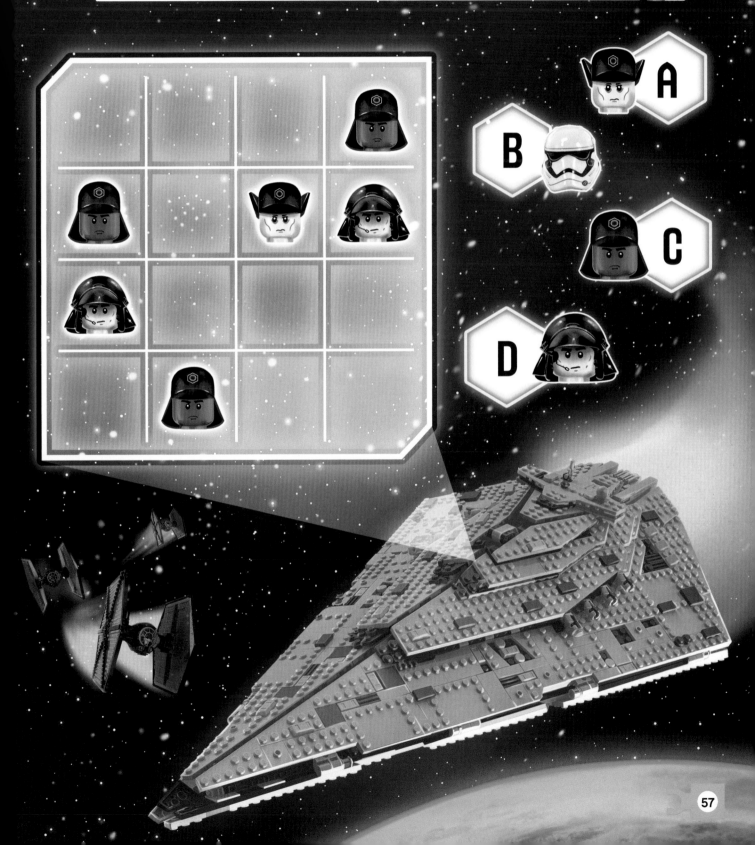

ANSWERS

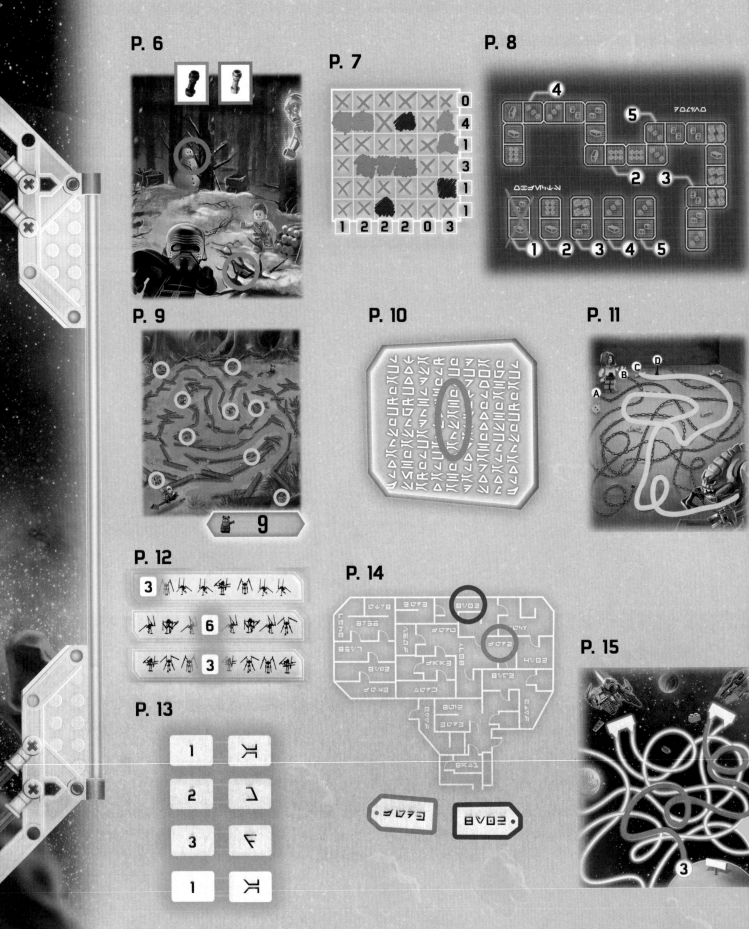

P. 16-17

P. 18-19

P. 20

P. 21

P. 22

P. 23

P. 26-27

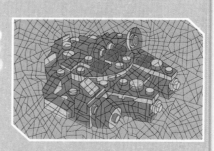

11

P. 30

P. 31

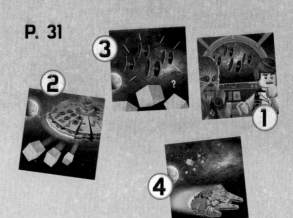

ANSWERS

P. 32

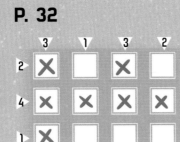

	3	1	3	2
2	X		X	
4	X	X	X	X
1	X			
2				

P. 33

CONFUSION CODE:
1 2 6 5 10
11 7 3 4
8 12

P. 34

P. 35

P. 36

P. 37

P. 38–39

P. 40

HAN SOLO	2	
1	LEIA	
DARTH VADER	3	
3	FINN	
REY	6	
1	SNOKE	

P. 41

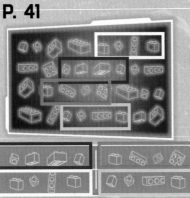

P. 42

P. 43

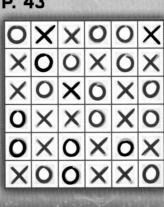

P. 45

P. 48-49

6F

P. 50

YODA | COUNT DOOKU | QUI-GON JINN | OBI-WAN KENOBI | ANAKIN

B 1 → **D** 2 → **A** 3 → **E** 4 → **C** 5

P. 51

11

7

P. 54

P. 52-53

6

7

THEY ARE NOT IMPERIAL OR FIRST ORDER STARSHIPS/VEHICLES.

P. 56

P. 57

A D B

B

A C B

B D A

P. 55

C